W YOU SEE ME, NOW YOU...

rissie Gittins was born in Lancashire and lives in South
ndon. Her children's poems have been broadcast on
C Radio 4, animated for Cbeebies television and widely
thologized. *Now You See Me, Now You ...* was shortlisted
r the first CLPE Poetry Award in 2003. Her second children's
etry collection *I Don't Want an Avocado for an Uncle* was
ortlisted for the CLPE Poetry Award 2007 and was a Poetry
ok Society Choice for the Children's Poetry Bookshelf. Two
Chrissie's children's poems won Belmont Poetry Prizes in
02; *The Powder Monkey* won the category for poems for
2 year olds and *Bradshaw Plots his Revenge* was a runner-
in the category for poems for 5-8 year olds. She has read
r children's poetry at the Aldeburgh Poetry Festival, the Hay
stival, the Edinburgh International Book Festival and the
ets House in New York. She also writes radio drama, and
s published two poetry collections and a collection of short
ories for adults. She tutors for the Arvon Foundation and is a
nember of the Poetry Society's Poetryclass team.
ww.chrissiegittins.co.uk

Gunnlaug Moen Hembury graduated from Birmingham City
University with a first class degree in illustration in 2000. She
now lives back in Norway, one hour's drive from Oslo. She has
illustrated for The Radio Times, The Guardian, The Financial
Times, Pizza Express and the Norwegian Health Department.
www.gunnlaug.co.uk

By the same author

Poetry for children
The Listening Station
Now You See Me, Now You …
I Don't Want an Avocado for an Uncle

Poetry for adults
A Path of Rice
Pilot
Armature
I'll Dress One Night as You

Short stories
Family Connections

Radio plays
Poles Apart
Starved for Love
Life Assurance
Dinner in the Iguanodon

Now You See Me,
Now You...

POEMS BY CHRISSIE GITTINS

ILLUSTRATIONS BY GUNNLAUG MOEN HEMBERY

First published in 2002
by Rabbit Hole publications
24 Elsinore Road, London SE23 2SL
Reprinted 2009

Designed by LOUP
Printed by Diamond, Dartford

ISBN 0-9543288-0-9

Some of the poems in this book have been published in:
A Path of Rice (Dagger Press, 1997)
The Listening Station (Dagger Press, 1998)
Join In...Or Else (Macmillan, 2000)
Snake Hotel (Macmillan, 2001)
The School Year (Macmillan, 2001)
Pilot (Dagger Press, 2001)
Poems are ... Private (Pearson Education, 2001)
The Works 2 (Macmillan, 2002)
The Top Secret Lives of Teachers (Macmillan, 2002)
Wandamania (Hodder Wayland, 2003)
Hubble Bubble (Hodder Wayland, 2003)
Dinos, Dodos and Other Dead Things (Macmillan, 2003)
Don't Panic: 100 Poems to Save You Life (Macmillan, 2003)
Read Me and Laugh (Macmillan, 2005)
Masala (Macmillan, 2005)
The Works 4 (Macmillan, 2005)
The Secret Lives of Teachers – 3 Books in 1 (Macmillan, 2005)
The Works Poems for Assembly (Macmillan, 2007)
Red Lorry, Yellow Lorry (Macmillan, 2007)
The Jumble Book (Macmillan, 2009)
The Works 8 (Macmillan, 2009)
Read Me At School (Macmillan, 2009)
*Michael Rosen's A-Z: The Very Best of Children's Poetry from
Agard to Zephania* (Puffin, 2009)

Death in the Poetry Library was The Sunday Poem, Independent
on Sunday, 17th November 2002

*With special thanks to Brian Morse, Moniza Alvi and the Arts
Council England for a Grant for the Arts to reprint this collection.*

CONTENTS

For Esther, Sam and Warren, with love

NOW YOU SEE ME, NOW YOU...
For Warren

I try not to make it too obvious,
sometimes I don't go in there for days,
but once, maybe three times a week,
I disappear to the garage –
my kids think I'm going through a phase.

I start by straightening the jars
of screws and nails and tacks,
I might take a rag to the window,
or give the table a wax.
But sooner or later I open the drawer
and sit down with the facts.

Last week I went to Thailand,
flew curtsey of B.A.,
wore a sarong on Koh Samui,
rode an elephant for the day.

Saturday was the Orkneys,
an eagle flew overhead,
I saw puffins take off from the cliff edge,
sleeping seals, pure white sands for a bed.

I'll never get over New York,
I'm definitely going back next year,
I watched American Football,
they even had decent beer.

But now I must pack up the brochures,
my wife will be home very soon,
if I don't put on the dinner,
she'll kick me half way to the moon.

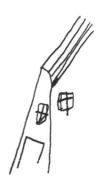

HIGH-CHAIR
for Alice Catherine

Arms up
Bib on
Eat up
Get down

Arms up
Bib on
Throw food
Mum down

Arms out
No bib
Get down
Throw up

Dad tries
No go
Head down
Give up

SAM, SAM, QUITE CONTRARY

Sam, Sam, quite, contrary,
bought a budgie,
wanted a canary.

Sam, Sam, quite contrary,
kissed Suzannah,
meant to kiss Mary.

Sam, Sam, quite contrary,
dressed as a pirate,
playing a fairy.

Sam, Sam, quite contrary,
ate dark chocolate,
says he likes dairy.

Sam, Sam, quite contrary,
shaved his head,
to make it hairy.

GETTING UP

Time to get up, Sam.

The sun shines through my red curtains
like an electric fire,
Noddy cocks his head beside my bed - tick tock,
I snuggle up to Mr Snowman.
He walks across my duvet, nice and warm.

Come on, Sam, time to get up.

Where did I put my t-shirt?
It was on the bookshelf,
maybe it ran for cover under the bed.
Oh look, there's my teddy, John.
What's it like living under there?

Sam, get yourself dressed,
you're going to be late for school.

Expect you'd like some breakfast,
would bread and honey do the trick?
Or mashed banana in a sandwich, yum.
I need to tie your bow around your neck.

Sam, if you're not down here in two
minutes, you're in big trouble.

Where's the armhole in this jumper?
I know I had another sock,
maybe Toucan knows who hid my trousers.
I know, I'll wear my Batman outfit,
without socks.

You can't go to school like that, Sam.

Why not? Why not? Why not?

THE TALE OF DOTTY CUDDLETUM

There was a young girl called Lottie
whose tum was ever so spotty,
she pulled up her vest
inspected her chest
and then went to sit on her potty.

The spots were all over her arms and her legs,
she even had one on her nose.
When she took off her socks
and wiggled her feet
she had seventeen spots on her toes.

'Don't worry' said Mummy,
'Don't worry' said Daddy,
'we'll go to the shop tomorrow
for a bottle of potion called calamine lotion
then we'll just see how it goes.'

By the end of the week,
the treatment complete,
Lottie was not quite so spotty.
She patted her tum and began to have fun.
From that day her nickname was Dotty.

THE NOODLE EATER

I am a noodle eater,
I eat them in the night,
I eat them by the basketful
and give my dad a fright.

I eat them dry,
I eat them wet,
I eat them upside-down.
And best of all I eat them with
an eyebrow-meeting-frown.

TWISTER HAMSTER

Twister sleeps in the day,
Esther sleeps at night.
Esther wakes in the morning,
gives Twister quite a fright
by poking her finger at Twister
who bites her thumb real hard.

Esther now has a plaster.
And she pulls away her finger a bit faster.

HARRY THE HAMSTER

Harry the hamster, in his ball,
rolled round the bedroom,
rolled round the hall.
He rolled to the bathroom,
he rolled to the stairs
where a huge teddy bear
took him clean unawares.

He rolled slap-bang into
the honey hall wall,
but that didn't stop him
for he was so small
and a whole world awaited
Harry in his ball.

On Monday he rolled down the garden,
on Tuesday he rolled down the road,
on Thursday he rolled down a bike path
till he was stopped in his tracks
by a toad.

On Friday he rolled to New Brighton,
on Saturday to warm Singapore,
on Sunday he yawned, climbed back
in his cage, and all day
simply rolled in his straw.

SNAIL SONG

For Alan, my postman, who slipped on a snail
and was off work for six weeks!

"I'm sick of being small," said the snail,
"Everyone around me is tall,
the milkman, the gas man, the woman with the paper –
I can leave a trail,
but it puts me in a vapour
that I am so small.

The postman comes at a quarter to nine,
I'm going to get him with a long line of slime,
I'll show them all how tall I can stand."

The postman came, the postman slipped.
His foot swole up like a zeppelin.
Then a thrush came along,
Sang a very pretty song,
And swallowed the snail in a second.

THE GIRL WHO LIVES
UNDER A STONE

She doesn't know the World Cup has started,
that Ginger Spice has left The Girls,
that Barbie Doll has got a boyfriend,
that bootlegs are *the* pair of pants to wear in town.

She knows her ants from her woodlice,
she knows when a frost hits the ground,
she knows that moss shines lime in moonlight,
she knows that moths don't leave a sound.

DUSK AT THE BOTANICAL
GARDENS, BATH

Magnolia buds stand proud of their stems
like the tips of cats' tails,
crocus close their cups.

A papaya sun pushes down on the rooves,
the moon is half a melting pancake.

THE HANDKERCHIEF TREE

This one's for the sniffles,
when your nose runs down to your mouth,
this one's for the blues,
when the sides of your mouth run south.

This one's for strawberry cheesecake icecream,
it's so good you just have to dribble,
this one's for your left-over-sandwich –
there was only time for a nibble.

This one goes round your knee
when you've fallen off your bike,
this one's for when you slip on the pitch –
but it was worth it for that strike.

This one's to give your Mum
when you start your first day at school,
and this one's for when you fall in love
and you feel an absolute fool.

PLAYGROUND IN THE RAIN

The tractor does not wobble on its spring,
the slide is not slid upon,
the helter skelter makes a solitary swirl,
the swings cannot remember when the sun
  last shone.

The benches wait for watching parents,
the dustbin's tummy rumbles,
the climbing frame train is going nowhere,
the sodden roundabout grumbles.

THE LISTENING STATION

It hears the wind that rushes through the trees
saying something of the sea,
it hears a moth leaving the ceiling,
it hears the thin pages of a book close,
it hears a late key turn in the door.

It hears an egg flop into a mixing bowl,
it hears the crack of a bended knee,
it hears a wash leather squeak down a window pane,
it hears an apple eaten to its rotten core.

It hears a pencil dragged across tissue paper,
it hears a pea-stick snapped in half,
it hears a mouth leave another mouth,
it hears a lion (or is it a child?) roar.

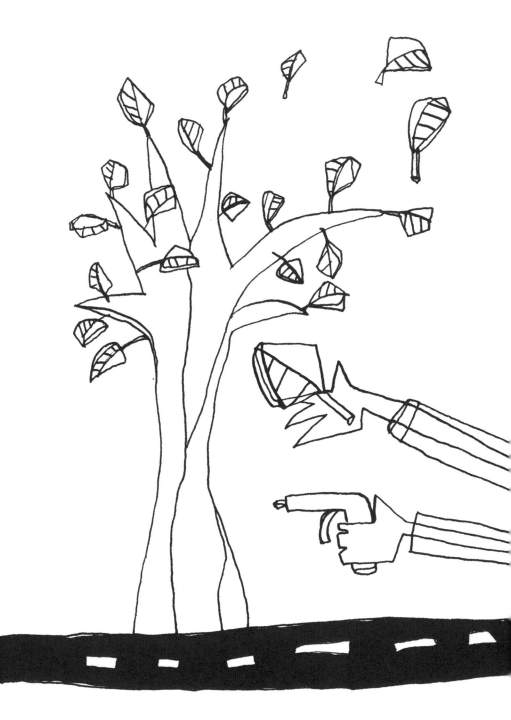

GILBERT AND HIS GLUE GUN

Gilbert has a glue gun,
he walks along the street,
and when he sees that leaves
are swirling round his feet,
he picks them up and sticks them back,
he leaves the pavement neat,
and tidy till the next day
when the trees have dropped some more,
then he waltzes down the avenues
sticking leaves back by the score.

In winter he makes glue,
in summer he has nothing to do,
in spring he strokes the buds
and generally admires the view.

His busy time is autumn,
he's rushed off his sticky feet,
so if you see Gilbert in the fall,
be sure to give him a treat.

BACK TO SCHOOL

The smell of mincemeat
on the stairs,

a queue of Year 2 waiting
to be shot by flashbulbs,

the stack and curve of
grey plastic chairs,

a gold bell chiming
the end of play-time,

pencil shavings curling
down the throat of the bin.

GILLIAN COSTIGAN

I wish I was Gillian Costigan,
with hair brushed sleek
and clothes that fit.
I wish I was Gillian Costigan
with money in my pocket every single week.

Her smile is wide,
her shoes have a shine,
she has friends to tea,
she laughs all the time.

I wish I was Gillian Costigan.
She has holidays in Greece,
her Dad loves her Mum,
she has nieces and nephews,
a Nan and a Gran,
her sarnies are thick
with hard cheese *and* ham.

I wish I was Gillian Costigan
with a slide in my hair,
a huge Mum to hug me,
a new top to wear.

TUUP THE STORY-TELLER

He counted us in on his African drum,
the story began, CRICK-CRACK.
A fish swam out of his moving hands,

a crow flew out of his mouth.
His finger-nails were razor talons,
his skull an eagle's head.

He rose from the sea
to look at the view,
he grew and grew and grew.

He made a sound
like a whistling sigh,
I know what he was, do you?

HIDDEN DEPTHS

Imagine my surprise –
my eyes had trouble believing,
there on the T.V. screen –
my teacher, stretching and breathing.

He looked almost bald,
his hair was shoved under a cap.
He dived in the water, he was off like the shot,
swimming lap after lap after lap.

He wasn't the fastest, I'll give you that,
but I had him down for a zimmer.
I couldn't have been more completely wrong,
Mr Smith is an Olympic swimmer!

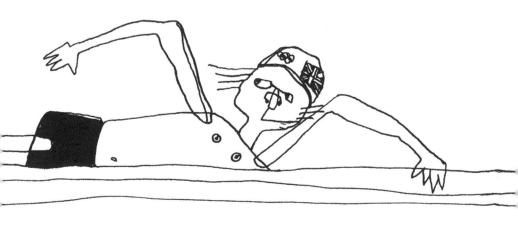

SWIMMING AT FOREST HILL

There's one who walks across the pool,
and two who natter at the side,
another shivers at the shallow end
standing half in half out.

Below the glass surface a swimsuit skirt
billows like a sea anemone.
The talking pair take a swim across, together,
but only when the way is clear,

they're scuppered when a shark dives in
with sleek black skin and goggles -
they know she'll do super-crawl, never looking up.
The walking woman tries a doggy paddle,

holds up her head and scampers for her life.
When her paw touches the far side
we all stop dead.
And slap our dripping flippers.

THE ROMAN BATHS

I threw a coin into the sacred pool
and made a secret wish.

If I tell the wish
then I will never have a friend,

If I tell the wish
then wars will never end,

If I tell the wish
my angel fish might die,

If I tell the wish
I will always wonder why

I threw a stone in the sacred pool
and made a secret wish.

DEATH IN THE POETRY LIBRARY
For M.R.

He stood between the stacks,
fishing out his reference.
Two flippant boys appeared,
paid little heed to the sign
'Please check aisle before...',
they wheeled the shelves together.
The poet, squashed between
authors L to M, wheezed.
Released, he lumbered
to the floor.

There was no blood.
His lines of verse
lapped along the corridor.

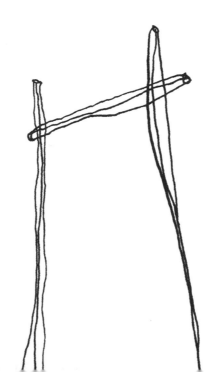

THE RUGBY TOURNAMENT

At the end of the last match of the season
there were four front teeth

poking out of the pitch,
two players had one arm each in a sling,

and there were possibly three little toes broken -
all on left feet.

Five sets of parents were hoarse from shouting
and couldn't go to work the next day.

Seven grans had hypothermia,
despite being wrapped in twelve tartan rugs.

Three little sisters have very snotty colds.
Everybody is dying for the next season to begin.

THE BRITISH MUSEUM PRINT ROOM

Van Gogh thought to be a preacher.
At twenty-one he came here and saw
the Rembrandt brown ink drawing over there,
then he did his own.

It lies in this glass case –
a splutter of rocks in the foreground,
a scruff of grass.
He drew every tree one behind the other
pulling right back to the horizon.

Dots become finer,
fields become thinner,
a track ripples to the right
while a train drags smoke to the left.

Stooks measure fields,
cypresses billow,
nothing is still.

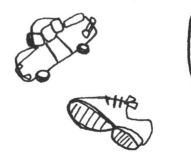

MESSAGES FROM THE HEART SCARAB
TO THE HEART

Don't tell I stole from my Mum's purse to buy the
    latest Jacqueline Wilson,
don't tell I ran in front of a car to avoid Barry Smith,
don't tell I stitched an aeroplane to the sky.

Don't tell I ate a whole bag of Thornton's
Continental Chocolates from my Auntie's cupboard,
don't tell I took a razor to lift the soles of the shoes
I was supposed to shine.

Don't tell I cut the string on my Daddy's
    garden chimes,
don't tell I put a dustbin through the science
    lab window,
don't tell I touched the curlew's egg.

*'The Heart Scarab was an essential Egyptian funerary amulet placed
over the heart. On the underside a spell is inscribed telling the heart to
say nothing during the Weighing of the Heart ceremony for fear that
it might make a guilty confession.'*
Horniman Museum.

THE FATE OF THE
BUTTERNUT SQUASH

Butter nut squash,
butter not squash,
better not squash the
butter nut squash,
better not nut the
butter nut squash.

Whoops! Who squished the
butter nut squash?

Now it's a squadge
of squelchy butter.

THE GOLDEN BELLY-BUTTON

Nattie had a funny tummy,
she could roll it in and out,

and sometimes from her navel
a golden coin would spout.

She sucked it in, she pushed it out
and there would roll the money -

but all that she could buy with it
was eiderdowns and honey.

GUTTED

These flats. I'm getting out of here.
I'm not going to be one of those they come round
collecting for wreaths for.

I want a room of my own.
Sean even gets hold of my underpants
if I don't watch him. And I'm sick of his City posters.

Telly's rubbish in the day. The adverts are alright.
I want to spear a dummy with a bayonet.
I bet my dad was in the army,
I bet he had boots and a gun.
I would stand to attention, I would
salute with my hand like this.

I wish I wasn't the eldest.
Sometimes I go to the fridge and drink
the baby's milk from her bottle.

DRIVEN TO DISTRACTION

I picked up a bus in the High Street
then put it down on the park,
I drove my Mum to Distraction -
that's the next town on from Dunkirk.

I stood, like a lemon, in a downpour
and someone gave me a squeeze,
I gave the cold shoulder to Matthew,
in minutes it started to freeze.

I got into hot water for fibbing,
the water didn't tell me a thing,
I threw bread at a tree for a lark
but instead it decided to sing.

I turned up my nose at the dinner,
it stayed like that for a week,
I tried not to be a wet blanket,
but my shoe laces started to leak.

PLANET NOTHING

I kneel up on our high-backed chair,
stretch my arms towards the sky,
pull the lever on the arm,
and at precisely a quarter to three
I am shot into the air.

Lakes soon become diamonds,
continents are omelettes,
the seas are just a squish of blue.

Space is layered with velvet,
the stars greet me,
the harvest moon smiles from ear to ear.

I land on Planet Nothing,
where there are no craters,
no creatures, no sparkling rocks,
and certainly no toy shops.

I cannot see a froth of cloud,
I cannot hear a phrase of music,
I cannot smell popcorn.

My journey home is double quick,
the carpet feels cosy beneath my icy feet.

SILLY CILLA

Cilla was a silly girl,
each time summer came round
she took off all her clothes
and lay down on the ground.

Her back went red,
her head boiled up,
her face looked like a prawn.
All she needed was a blink of sun
and a tiny bit of lawn.

Her skin would hurt,
her skin would sting,
but still our Cilla lay there,
until one day she disappeared
into a pink cloud of hot air.

The cloud was stacked with shelves
of lotion, oil and spray,
factor three hundred and twelve,
to be worn all through the day.

Now Cilla is more sensible,
she oils and rubs and sprays,
and goes inside if she starts to feel
in a bit of a sun-made daze.

In fact she's bored of sunbathing,
she prefers the cool of the night,
next year she's even thinking
of staying all-over completely white.

THE WELL-TRAVELLED TORTOISE

I am a tortoise from Turkey,
I lived in the hills of Kalkan,
my name over there was Mustafa,
my owners here call me Ken.

I would squaffle in the leaves on the slopes,
taking days from A to B,
the sun beat down on my back,
my nostrils were full of the sea.

Here in Catford it's different,
I live in a four-sided pen,
I walk the ten-metre circumference
and then walk round it again.

Instead of the calling to prayers
I hear the South Circular cars,
the sky is filled with neon,
there are hardly any stars.

I miss the smell of pine,
bougainvillaea dripping purple and red,
but here I get lots of attention,
and I admit it has gone to my head.

THE POWDER MONKEY

This is the moment I dread,
my eyes sting with smoke,
my ears sing with cannon fire.
I see the terror rise inside me,
coil a rope in my belly to keep it down.
I chant inside my head to freeze my nerve.

Main mast, mizzen mast, foremast,
belfry, capstan, waist.

We must keep the fire coming.
If I dodge the sparks
my cartridge will be safe,
if I learn my lessons
I can be a seaman,
if I close my eyes to eat my biscuit
I will not see the weevils.

Main mast, mizzen mast, foremast,
shot lockers, bowsprit, gripe.

Don't stop to put out that fire,
run to the hold,
we must fire at them
or they will fire at us.

Main mast, mizzen mast, foremast,
belfry, capstan, waist.

My mother never knew me,
but she would want to know this -
I can keep a cannon going,
I do not need her kiss.

Before 1794 children aged 6 upward went to sea.
After 1794 the minimum age was 13.

MIKE'S MOUNTAIN BARBEQUE

On Monday a midwife toad
jumps through raindrops from the hermitage
to watch Mike barbeque –
a green gingham oven glove.

On Tuesday three yellow butterflies
with clouded judgment get a lift on a snowflake
to watch Mike barbeque –
the pig bin.

On Wednesday five underprivileged crickets
fly on the wind from the San Pedro valley
to watch Mike barbeque –
a lifetime's supply of chewing gum.

On Thursday eleven wasps from the post box
ignore the thunder
to watch Mike barbeque –
the neighbour's washing line.

On Friday fourteen roe deer
spring from the sunshine in a nearby field
to watch Mike barbeque –
a three-legged clog.

On Saturday seventeen gruff griffon vultures
drop in from Dobres, not a care for the frost,
to watch Mike barbeque –
a relief map of the Picos.

On Sunday Mike ski jumps
over the cable car at Fuente Dé.
The pressure is low, the sky is clear,
the snow is as firm as a boned leg of lamb.

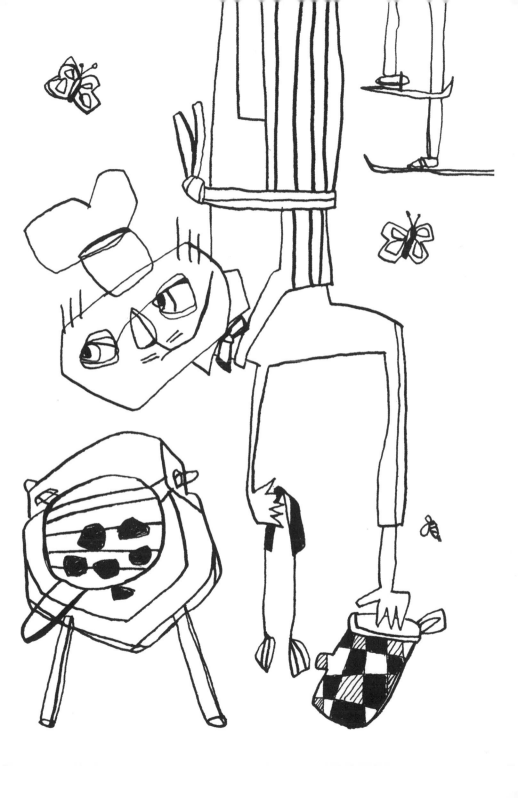

BRADSHAW PLOTS HIS REVENGE

As if being sunk in a bowl of soapy water
  wasn't enough,
now I'm pegged by my left ear
between blue shorts
and a pair of jogging bottoms.

I'm dry to my nose,
my legs are sodden,
and I'm dripping from my woolly toes.

I must hang here while they go
climbing castles,
skimming stones,
poking jellyfish.
Then I'm expected to listen to their adventures
when they get home!

Well I won't!
I will shut my ears,
purse my lips
and clench my fists.
They won't know the difference.

BEACH FOR RUKSAR

This beach has blonde sand sieved as fine
  as flour,
pebbles in sixteen shades of blue,
smooth black rock which shines with every tide.

Lines of limpets shelter in the cracks,
a pool appears with waving crabs and
  swaying weed.
There's bladder wrack and razor shells,
and waves which rise and crash
and bubble to the shore.

At first the sea feels icy cold,
  you scream and run away.
"Come back Ruksar," it says to you,
"Try again, be bold."

You teeter on the edge a while
then stretch your arms and launch into the surf.
Your eyes are bright,
you smile out loud,
your body shakes with watery mirth.

THE TRAVELLING WARDROBE
For Rosemary

Sometimes it stands in a desert -
waves of sand lapping over its feet.
It slips a tweed overcoat, silk lined,
over a dipping dune.

Sometimes it stands on a glacier,
one foot stuck in a crevasse.
The briefest of satin-edged slips
slides from the half open door.

Sometimes it stands on a prairie,
waist high in chafing wheat.
Six pairs of white cotton baby socks
fly in the wind and the heat.

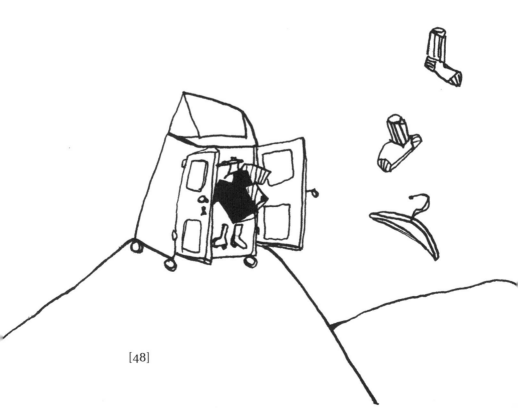

PUNCTUATE THAT LUNCH
YOU ATE

Punctuate that lunch you ate
last Thursday in the caff,

those beans would like a comma
and those sausages a dash.

Not to mention that the egg
wants a curly question mark,

and if the chips don't get one too
they'll get in a terrible nark.

The tomatoes want quotation marks,
the mushrooms are on the hop –

because all they want to see
is a brown sauce squirt full stop.

ME, MYSELF, I

You are a very important person,
You always have a CAPITAL 'I',
You are a very important person,
I speak no word of a lie,
You are a very important person,
Whether you're a cool girl or a gorgeous guy,
You're a very important person,
You deserve a CAPITAL 'I'.

In fact, without a doubt,
You deserve a CAPITAL 'I'
Which climbs straight through the ceiling
And hits the clear blue sky
Where a dragonfly is singing,
"Can I have a CAPITAL 'I'?"

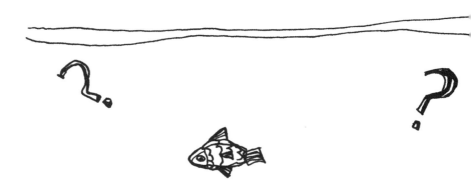

THE QUESTION MARK SHARK

There's a shark who lives deep in the ocean,
who jumps out to look at your work,
and if he sees there's a question,
he checks for a question mark.

If he sees one he dives to the next,
but if he sees you forget,
he eats up the question with relish,
showing not one sign of regret.

His belly is full of questions,
which writhe and leap in the dark,
"Oh why," those questions ask,
"didn't you give me a question mark?"

EXCLAMATION MARK PARK

If you want to say something scary, (Help!)
or your dog has a good old bark, (Woof!)
take a stroll down the end of your street,
where you'll find Exclamation Mark Park.

There they stand shoulder to shoulder,
a stick with a dot underneath,
they're dying for you to pick them,
for that they'd give their eyeteeth.

You use them for surprise and big feelings,
"That's fantastic!" "I really like that!"
"Good heavens!" "Look out!" "Cor Blimey!"
"Go away!" "Oh no!" "There's a rat!"

Remember the park in the evening,
especially when it's starting to rain,
the exclamation marks lean on the railings,
saying, "I don't want to go there again!"

WARTS AND ALL

A sentence can be very long,
a sentence can be short,
but at the end of every sentence
you'll find a jet black wart.

A verruca if you like,
which gets stuck between your toes,
but this dot sticks between sentences,
and it never ever goes.

It stops the end of a sentence
from running on and on,
a – full stop dot,
at the end of every one.

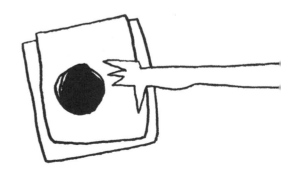

APPROACHING APOSTROPHES

*For Tony, my window cleaner, who had 32,000 cards
printed with extra apostrophes!*

The apostrophe is a tricky thing,
it swims across the page –
a tadpole in its infancy
at a very early stage.

It doesn't know quite where to stop
and needs a little steering,
there are three rules which it must use
to stop the pages teeming.

If there's a letter missing,
when two words are squeezed to one,
then the apostrophe stands in between,
so 'I have gone' becomes 'I've gone'.

The second rule shows belonging,
so when Kylie loses her mack,
and teacher says, "Is this Kylie's?"
we know Kylie's mack is back.

If there are two Kylies,
and both Kylies lose their mack,
when teacher writes "Are these Kylies' ? "
she has two macks to give back.

The last rule's about using plurals,
when there's more than one of a thing,
it's used with numbers and letters
and here we can go with a zing ...

Is that 10B's football?
Mind your p's and q's,
How many 6's in that box of wellies?
How many 4's in the shoes?

Julian got two A's in maths,
Frederick got two D's,
I like s's – the way they curl,
my friend, she likes t's.

So don't forget to train your tiddler,
don't let it be a tadpole lout,
and a final note, if you're not quite sure –
when in doubt leave apostrophes out!

PARADIDDLE 1

Paradiddle, paradiddle,
stick it in your brain,
paradiddle, paradiddle,
drum until you're sane.

PARADIDDLE 2

Paradiddle, paradiddle,
such a such a fiddle diddle,
hit it on the sides
then bash it in the middle.

Say it quick and say it now,
say it with a wobble wiggle.

*A paradiddle is a drumming pattern. These two
were written with Esther after she had played her
paraddidle repertoire on her drum kit.*

FREYA'S NEW PAIR OF SHOES

Freya's feet were very small,
in fact she usually wore tied-up leaves,
but since it was nearly winter,
she bought herself some shoes.

The shoes were black, the shoes were shiny,
they strapped across her feet,
the heels were strong and clicked along,
the buckles very neat.

When she put them on and sang a song
she rose up in the air,
feet first she flew with a swishing sound
followed by her hair.

She landed on a treetop,
overlooking a glistening lake,
when she flew again she landed
in her best friend's birthday cake.

A third flight proved quite dangerous,
she flew right across the sea
and landed in a fishing boat,
on the fisherman's knobbly knee.

By this time she was exhausted,
it was nearly time to sleep,
so she flew right under her duvet,
where her dozy sleep was deep.

POSSIBLE PRESENTS

The lick of a tall ice cream
and the first burnt nose of summer.

The jumper which shrunk in the wash
back to its usual size.

A bowl of red tulips
which curl up their petals at night.

A camouflaged frog jumping
between caramel leaves.

Bread baked this morning
spread with Somerset butter.

The blackbird which sings in the tree
each day at a quarter to four.

THE ICE MAN

He slid into our classroom –
a six-foot man in a block of ice.
Cool, or what?
We stood him near the radiator –
a pool of water spread across the floor.

The tip of his nose,
the back of his hands,
then his shoulders began to show.
The water lapped around our feet.

Mark went home to get his swimming gear,
Sureya made a fleet of boats,
Esther floated up to the window.
Our teacher gave up on the Egyptians
and blew up a lilo.

Just before the water reached the top of the door
the Ice Man began to drink,
he slurped and gulped and swallowed and gurgled
until the room was completely dry.
His mouth unfroze to a smile,
his chest heaved with a sigh,
then he left the room as silently as he'd arrived.

There is a damp patch where he stood
which never quite goes away.

THE SHORTEST DAYS
for Suze

How dark is the morning,
how dark is the day,
will the sun shoulder
the darkness away?

The cars shine their headlights
at lunch-time,
the dawn stays the same
until dusk, snow sits -
tall hats on the seedheads,
an afternoon dew takes a rest.

How dark is the evening,
how dark is the day,
will the sun soon
shiver the darkness away?

THE 'I'M NOT TIRED' DANCE
For Moniza

I've been to the park to-day,
swung on the swings,
slid down the slide,
climbed a tower,
I'm not tired.

I've been to school to-day,
run in the playground,
listened to teacher,
written a poem,
I'm not tired.

I got home to-day,
watched some telly,
drew a picture,
read my book,
I'm not tired.

I've eaten my dinner,
thrown my clothes,
had my bath,
cleaned my teeth,
coloured my nails,
talked to the gerbils,
danced on my bed,
blown my nose
and I'M NOT TIRED.

GOVERNMENT HEALTH WARNING

Don't squash peas on your knees,
Don't grate carrot on a parrot,
Don't tangle pears in your nostril hairs,
Never risk a quid on a squid.

Don't pour bottled beer in your ear.
Never slice apple pies on your thighs,
Never wash your pullovers with yesterday's leftovers,
Don't entice a bowl of egg fried rice.

Don't assume that tarragon's a paragon,
Or try to run faster than a bag of spinach pasta,
Don't try a lunge at Victoria sponge,
A cake with a steak is a mistake.

Bravado never works with avocado,
A flickin's not the thing to give to chicken,
Don't go and stutter on the b-b-b-b-butter,
Never feed mice on ice.

Careful not to ravage a coy savoy cabbage,
Never have a tussle with a mussel,
Don't ever hurry with a spicy prawn curry,
Don't boast about your buttered toast.

Don't pour jelly in your welly,
Don't dribble tagliatelle on your older brother's belly.
Never do the tango with a ripe and juicy mango,
If you do then you're sure to pay the price!

WHAT DOES POETRY DO?

It nosedives from the top of the fridge
into a bowl of rapids,

it crawls along the floor
and taps you on the knee,

it changes the colour of a room,

it puts great wheezing slices of life
into bun trays, with or without punctuation.

It manages this all by itself.